A barn owl can't move its eyes side to side like we can, but **it can twist its head to see behind**. A barn owl chick's fluffy down is replaced with feathers when it is 12 weeks old. Then it is ready to fly.

Barn Owl

A **brown bear has thick fur** with a large hump on its shoulders. The brown bear is one of the largest North American land mammals. The mother bear will sleep all winter, not even waking up to give birth to her cubs!

Brown Bear

A male deer is called a buck and a female deer is called a doe.

A white-tailed deer shows the white under its tail to signal alarm. A **baby deer is called a fawn**. After it is born, the little fawn stays hidden in the grass for one week until it is strong enough to walk with its mother.

White-tailed Deer

Wild Rabbit

A rabbit's teeth wear down as it nibbles its food, but they keep regrowing. The rabbit's **eyes are on either side of its head** so it can see all around. A baby rabbit is called a kit.

Cold Climate Cuties

Reindeer

Reindeer hooves change for the seasons. In the summer, their footpads get softer. In the winter, the pads shrink, which shows more of the hooves. This helps the reindeer **grip in the ice** and snow.

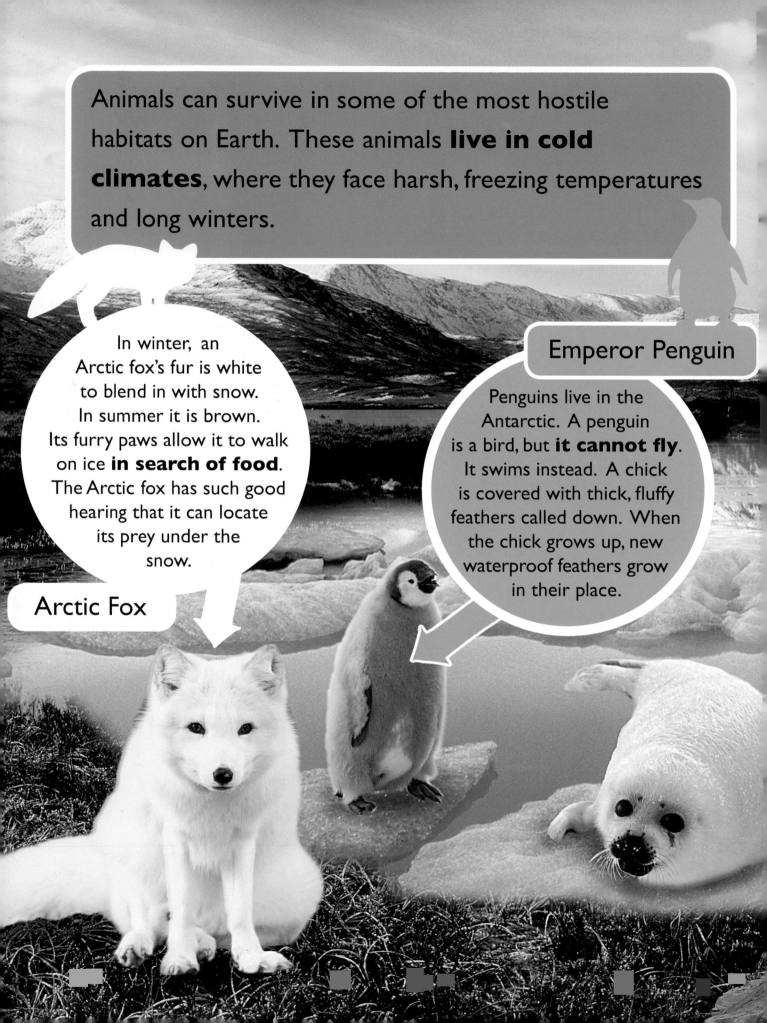

Animals can survive in some of the most hostile habitats on Earth. These animals **live in cold climates**, where they face harsh, freezing temperatures and long winters.

In winter, an Arctic fox's fur is white to blend in with snow. In summer it is brown. Its furry paws allow it to walk on ice **in search of food**. The Arctic fox has such good hearing that it can locate its prey under the snow.

Arctic Fox

Emperor Penguin

Penguins live in the Antarctic. A penguin is a bird, but **it cannot fly**. It swims instead. A chick is covered with thick, fluffy feathers called down. When the chick grows up, new waterproof feathers grow in their place.

Polar Bear

The polar bear lives in the Arctic. Its white coat is made of two types of fur. Short woolly fur keeps it warm, and longer hollow hairs keep out the water. Under its fur, the polar bear's **skin is black**, like its nose, tongue, paws, and claws.

Harp Seal

A newborn seal has a fluffy white coat of fur. It loses that coat after three weeks and grows a thick **layer of fat called blubber**. A seal can stay underwater for up to 15 minutes.

Wolves **live in groups** known as packs made up of around six to ten animals. They speak to each other by howling. Most gray wolves live in Alaska, Canada, and Asia. In the wild, gray wolves can live up to 8 years.

Wolf

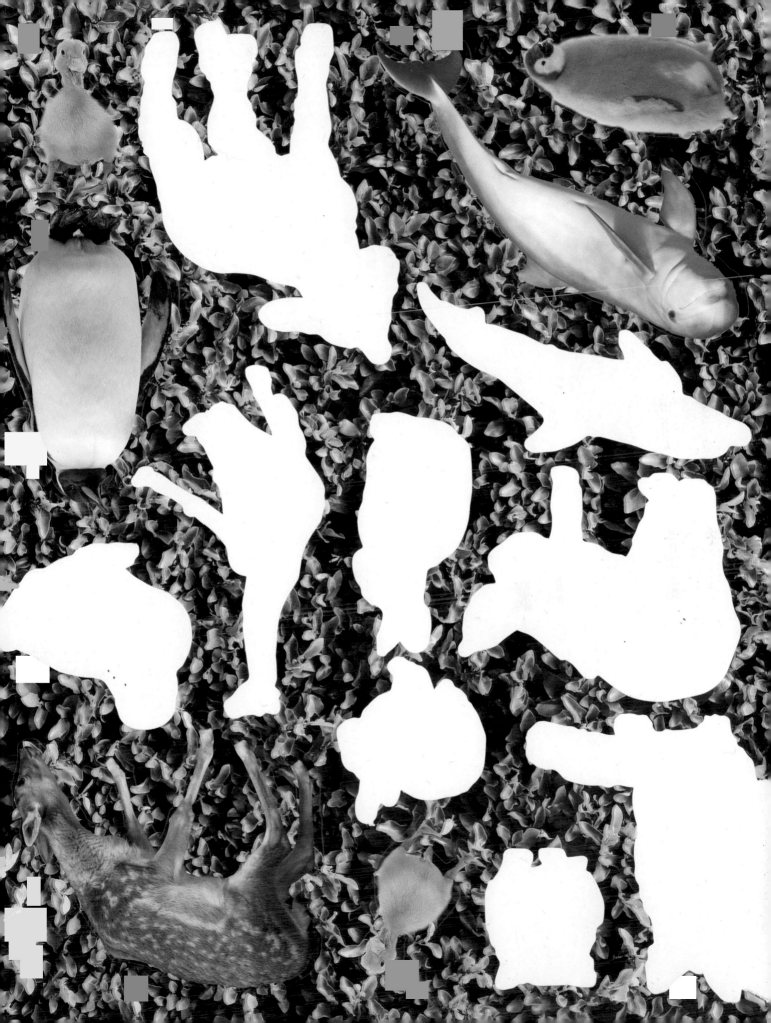

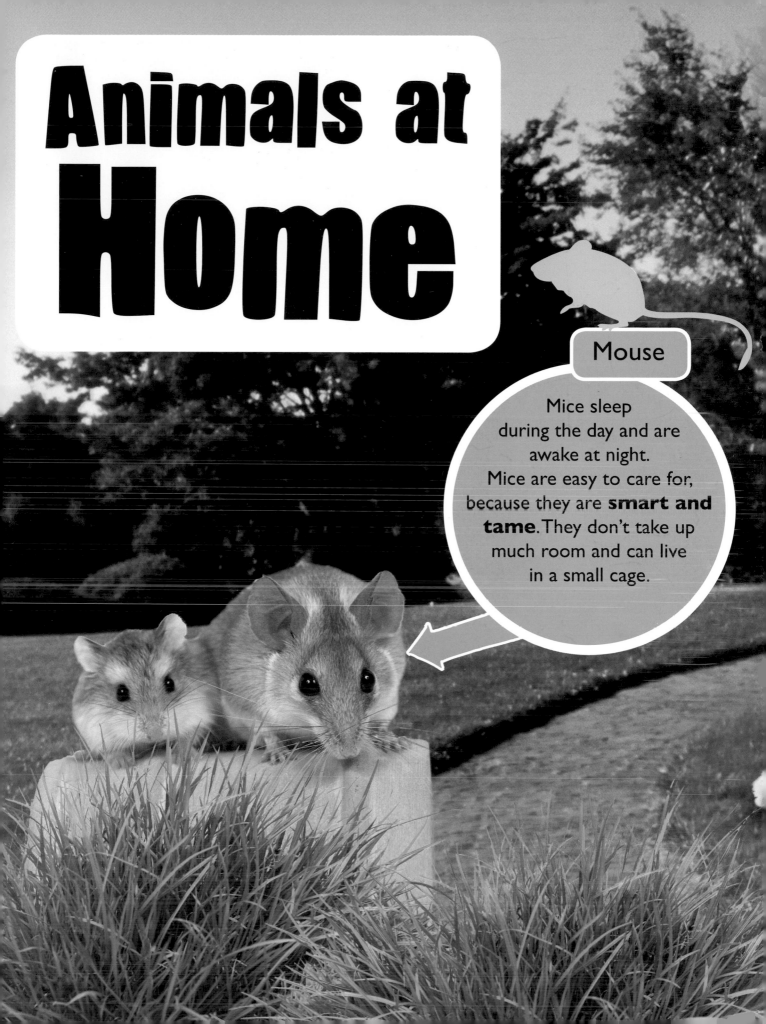

Animals at Home

Mouse

Mice sleep during the day and are awake at night. Mice are easy to care for, because they are **smart and tame**. They don't take up much room and can live in a small cage.

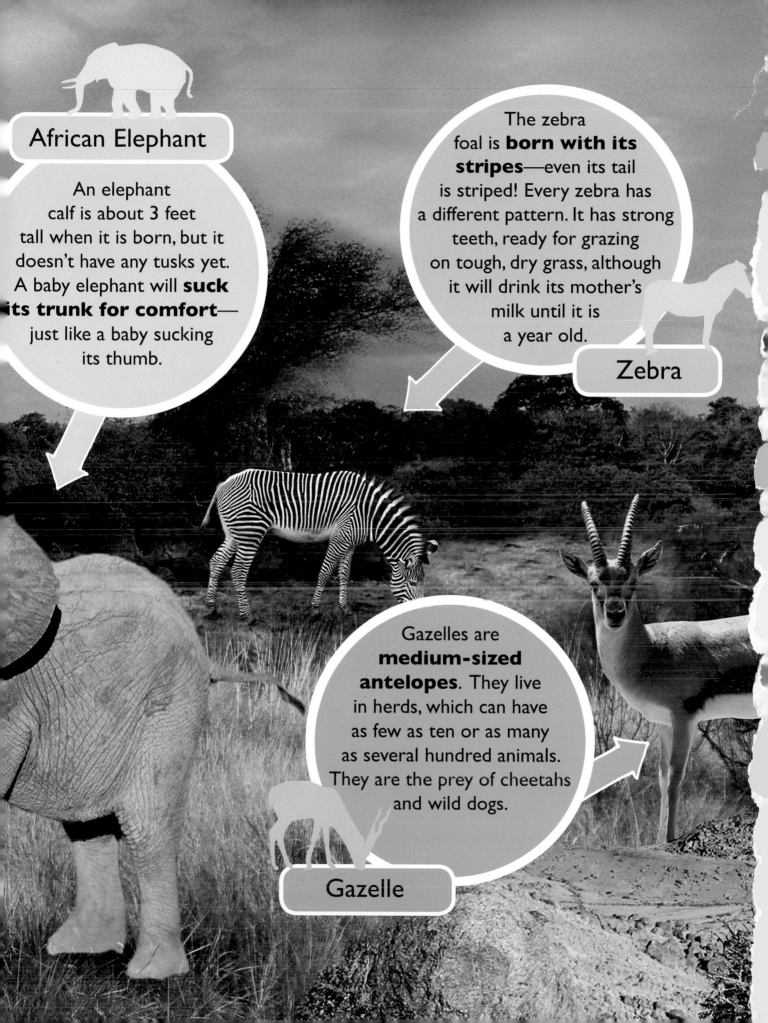

African Elephant

An elephant calf is about 3 feet tall when it is born, but it doesn't have any tusks yet. A baby elephant will **suck its trunk for comfort**—just like a baby sucking its thumb.

The zebra foal is **born with its stripes**—even its tail is striped! Every zebra has a different pattern. It has strong teeth, ready for grazing on tough, dry grass, although it will drink its mother's milk until it is a year old.

Zebra

Gazelles are **medium-sized antelopes**. They live in herds, which can have as few as ten or as many as several hundred animals. They are the prey of cheetahs and wild dogs.

Gazelle

Humans can keep many creatures at home as pets. **We care for our pets**, feed them, play with them, and even take them for walks. See how these cute animals live at home.

Dogs are popular pets. They need a lot of exercise and must be taken for regular walks. Their coats are coarse hair with soft downy hair underneath. Dogs can be great companions and **loyal to their owners.**

Dog

Cat

A cat is a creature that can ok after itself. It can clean d exercise itself, making it a fect pet. It **can see in the ark** and can hunt mice and ats. A cat can live for up to 20 years. It purrs when relaxed.

The ancient Egyptians had domestic cats, and thought of them as sacred animals.

Hamster

A hamster is a small furry rodent. As a pet, it is kept in a cage in-doors. It eats seeds, cereal, fruit, and vegetables. A hamster **has large cheeks** like sacks, where it stores its food to eat later.

Monkeys and apes are **part of the primate family**. The easiest way to tell a monkey from an ape is that monkeys generally have a tail. These friendly mammals are found in tropical forests and wet savannas. They spend most of their time in trees, but they can also live on the ground.

DiscoveryFact™

Chimps, just like humans, are sociable, use tools, and can learn from each other.

Baboon

in grou[p] to 50 individuals. noisy, curious animals. They use **over 30 noises to speak**, ranging from grunts to barks to screams.

Primate Friends

Chimps are territorial and **throw large sticks and branches** at enemies. Chimpanzees live in groups called troops, with up to 80 individuals.

Chimpanzee

Guinea Pig

A guinea pig is
a rodent. As a pet
it lives in a cage and needs
plenty of room. It is a lively
creature that **speaks with
high squeaks**. Its natural
food is grass, but it will
also eat hay, dry mix food,
fruit, and vegetables.

Rabbit

A rabbit
makes a good pet,
because it can be **friendly
and playful**. It can be kept
in a hutch outside, but some
rabbits live indoors. It needs
fresh straw to sleep in.
It eats hay, rabbit mix, fresh
fruit, and vegetables.

In the Sea

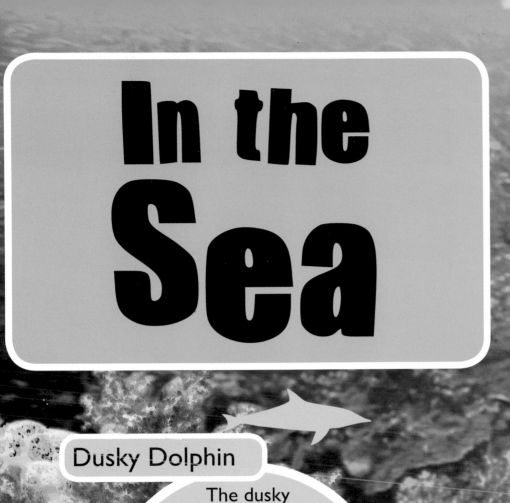

Dusky Dolphin

The dusky dolphin is known for its **high leaps out of water**. It likes to ride along with boats, doing up to 50 acrobatic leaps one after the other. The back of the dolphin is dark gray or black, and the dorsal fin is two-toned.

Squirrel Monkey

Squirrel monkeys roam around the treetops in large troops of 20 to 100, making a lot of noise! They **feed on small insects** and fruit, and also like nectar from flowers.

The Rhesus monkey spends most of its time on the ground, although it is an **excellent climber and swimmer**. It can adapt to many habitats, including human communities.

Rhesus Monkey

This monkey can fit in the palm of your hand. It lives in small groups, feeding on tree sap, insects, and sometimes small fruit. It is also known as "little lion" because of the **fur around its head**.

Pygmy Marmoset

"*Orangutan*" is a Malay word that means "person of the forest." Orangutans can live for up to 50 years. **Strong, long arms** help them swing from branch to branch. At night, they sleep in the treetops.

Orangutan

Golden lion tamarins live mostly in the trees. They sleep in hollows at night. They have long fingers, which help them **catch insects, lizards, and birds**.

Golden Lion Tamarin

The world's deep oceans are home to many of the most fascinating creatures. You can find playful mammals and "fin-footed" animals doing underwater somersaults. **Dive into the deep** with these amazing dolphins and seals.

The gray seal is one of the rarest species of seal in the world. Nearly half the population live in the seas around England. The **hands and feet are webbed flippers** or "fin-footed," with 5 claws on each flipper.

Gray Seal